THE GAMBOLS

BOOK No. 36

by

Barry Appleby

£1·75

GAYE FINDS THAT SOME OF THE RECIPES IN COOK BOOKS ARE A BIT EXPENSIVE TO MAKE — BUT IT ALL DEPENDS ON WHAT GEORGE HAS IN HIS WINE CUPBOARD

IT WAS HIGH TIME WE HAD A NEW CAR

It is always sad to part with an old car – it's like parting with an old friend and it's surprising how well they seem to run on the last day that you are their owner!

SHOPPING FOR
CLOTHES IS VERY
MUCH A WOMAN'S
INTEREST —
BUT MEN ALSO
BUY CLOTHES
YOU KNOW

3609

WE'VE LEARNT THAT IT'S EASY TO KEEP OUR NEPHEW AND NIECE HAPPY WHEN THEY COME TO VISIT US — ALL WE HAVE TO DO IS TO KEEP THEM WELL FED

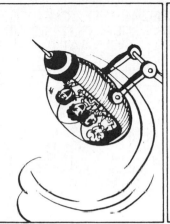

The GAMBOLS
by Barry Appleby

GOOD EVENING— I'VE CALLED FOR MIGGY

SHE PROMISED TO LET ME TAKE HER OUT TO DINNER...SO THAT WE COULD GET TO KNOW ONE ANOTHER

BUT CANDIDLY I WAS EXPECTING SOMEBODY OLDER FOR A PEN PAL

© 1986
Barry Appleby

3646

YOU'VE BEEN FIGHTING AGAIN

YES....I DON'T USUALLY LIKE GIRLS

BUT SOMEHOW MIGGY'S DIFFERENT

© 1986
Barry Appleby

3571

AND NOW FOR A FEW LARGER CARTOONS WHICH
YOU MAY NOT HAVE SEEN BEFORE

723

733

735

734

792

852

722

718

GEORGE! TAKE OFF YOUR DIRTY BOOTS BEFORE YOU COME INTO THE HOUSE

I'VE JUST POLISHED THE FLOOR

OH DEAR— HE CAN'T HEAR ME

AH WELL, I'LL LEAVE HIS SLIPPERS OUT FOR HIM

THAT'S FUNNY! I DON'T REMEMBER LEAVING MY SLIPPERS THERE WHEN I PUT ON MY WELLIES

721

719

THE BIGGEST EVENT IN OUR LIVES THIS YEAR
WAS THE DAY GAYE DECIDED TO JOIN THE RANKS
OF THE THOUSANDS AND THOUSANDS OF
HOUSEWIVES AND TAKE A PART TIME JOB

3690

3691

Several girls wrote about this cartoon – all saying that only a man could have designed the average typist's desk and they all complained that it was most embarrassing the way that this kind of desk showed the secretary's legs.

YESTERDAY

TODAY

AH YES.. HERE IT IS... I KNEW IT WOULD BE IN THE PAPERS

...AN AGREEMENT WAS FINALLY REACHED AFTER A LONG HARD DAY'S NEGOTIATION BETWEEN MANAGEMENT AND UNION LEADERS....

©1987 Barry Appleby

3791

PSST... QUICK

NO-I'M AFRAID HE'S NOT IN HIS OFFICE AT THE MOMENT

©1987 Barry Appleby

WELL, YOU WOULDN'T WANT TO MAKE A LIAR OUT OF ME .. WOULD YOU?

3798

WE LOVE HAVING MIGGY AND FLIVVER TO STAY WITH US— THEY'RE NO TROUBLE AT ALL—PROVIDED WE KEEP AN EYE ON THEM ALL THE TIME

THE CHILDREN ARE COMING TO STAY WITH US TOMORROW

© 1987 Barry Appleby

3760

© 1987 Barry Appleby

AND THIS IS ONLY THEIR FIRST DAY HERE

3846

HOW OLD WERE YOU BEFORE YOU REALISED YOU WERE ONLY A GIRL?

3762

GAYE, CAN I HAVE A DRINK PLEASE?

TAKE THIS TO YOUR UNCLE PLEASE

WHAT I WANT TO KNOW IS **WHERE** DID SHE LEARN ABOUT TOPLESS WAITRESSES?

©1987 Barry Appleby

3766

3647

GARDENING IS A BIT LIKE HOUSEWORK—
NO SOONER IS IT DONE THAN YOU HAVE
TO START ALL OVER AGAIN

© 1986 Barry Appleby

3562

© 1986 Barry Appleby

20-7

IF YOU CAN'T BE HAPPY ON HOLIDAY—
WHEN CAN YOU BE ?

DENTISTS ARE SURELY THE VERY NICEST OF PEOPLE — SO WHY DOES EVERYBODY AVOID MEETING THEM?

3830

3582

SURELY YOU'RE NOT LEAVING YET

IT'S ONLY JUST GONE MIDNIGHT

WON'T YOU **EVER** LEARN TO KEEP YOUR MOUTH SHUT?

©1986 Barry Appleby

3549

WELL — **YOU** INVITED THEM

I THOUGHT **EVERYBODY** KNEW THAT YOU DIDN'T INVITE THE PARSLEYS ON THE SAME EVENING THAT YOU INVITED THE SPROUTS

©1986 Barry Appleby

3601

CHRISTMAS COMES BUT ONCE
A YEAR — PITY ISN'T IT?

NOW I'M TOO TIRED TO ENJOY OUR PARTY

21-12

BUTCHER

LAST MINUTE LISTS

GIFTS

ONLY TWO OR THREE MORE ITEMS DARLING AND THEN YOU CAN START YOUR CONVALESCENCE

3751

© 1987 Barry Appleby

THAT'S ALL WE HAVE ROOM FOR NOW— AND SO
WE COLLECT OUR CARTOONS AND LEAVE YOU—
BUT THERE WILL BE MORE TOMORROW IN THE
DAILY EXPRESS OR THE SUNDAY EXPRESS

Published by Express Newspapers Limited, Fleet Street, London, EC4P 4JT, and printed by Richard Clay Ltd, Bungay, Suffolk